The Best Manchester United Trivia Book Ever

300+ Interesting Trivia Questions and Random, Shocking, Fun Facts Every Red Devils Fan Needs to Know

House of Ballers

YOUR FREE BONUS!

- What did Materazzi say to earn a headbutt from Zidane on the biggest stage of them all?
- Who got shot for scoring an own goal at the World Cup?
- What did Maradona reveal on his autobiography about the 'Hand of God'?

Find out by scanning the QR Code below
with your smartphone:

Contents

INTRODUCTION

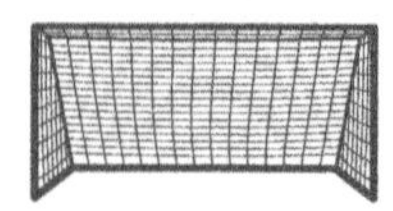

Football is the biggest, most-watched, and probably the most lucrative sport globally, and Manchester United FC is one of its biggest clubs. In their classic red, white, and black jerseys, the Red Devils have one of the largest and most loyal fanbases in the history of competitive sport.

Depending on who you ask, the number of Manchester United fans in the world ranges from 75 million to a few hundred million or a billion people. What is not in doubt, though, is that allegiance to Manchester United cuts across every city in the world. As evidenced by over 70 million followers on social media and more than 262 official fan clubs in 89 countries, many of these fans have a religious devotion to Manchester United, and it is easy to see why.

Over nearly the last century and a half, some of the most notable names in world football have pitched their tents at the Theatre of Dreams. From the wizardry of George Best to the sheer quality of Sir Bobby Charlton; from the grit of Roy Keane to the finesses of Cristiano Ronaldo, Old Trafford has been home to a conveyor belt of footballers who dazzled and thrilled millions on the way to success.

And it is not just the players that the fans want to see. Some of the managers and head coaches at Manchester United have had a larger-than-life image. Sir Matt Busby, Sir Alex Ferguson and Jose Mourinho certainly command(ed) a cult-like devotion worldwide.

Sir Matt Busby had the Busby Babes who overcame all in front of them. Sir Alex Ferguson, the most successful manager in the club's history, won 38 major trophies with a swashbuckling attacking philosophy that left opponents confounded and kept the fans on the edge of their seats. Jose Mourinho kept up a stream of catchy and flashy soundbites that always had that extra edge in them. All delivered success to the club!

Manchester United has conquered the continent thrice in dramatic fashion; a dozen FA Cup titles and numerous other titles also tell a story of excellence. The club holds the record for the most league titles won in the most lucrative and most popular league in the world.

So, it is not a surprise that the club is also a commercial juggernaut that commands highly lucrative deals and brand sponsorships. The Deloitte Football Money League and Forbes List of Most Valuable Clubs have constantly put Manchester United in the top 4 of the biggest revenue-generating football clubs in the world.

In its 143 years of existence, the club has had enough history of glory, pain, drama, controversy and everything else in-between to make a hundred Hollywood movies. For each shocking defeat to bitter rivals, there are a dozen great nights at Old Trafford. For the most successful era, the Munich disaster still hurts today.

Yet, despite recent struggles and the growth of their city rivals, Manchester United remains arguably the biggest club in England. They dwarf everyone else in titles won, commercial and worldwide appeal and sheer dramatic value.

The exploits of the Holy Trinity of George Best, Denis Law and Sir Bobby Charlton captured the fans' minds in a way few players can. The twinkle-toed young Cristiano Ronaldo left opponents reeling in his wake. The bravery of Bryan Robson and Steve Bruce had opponents quaking in their boots. The Class of 92 grew into the backbone of the most successful era in English football history with one-club men like Paul Scholes, Ryan Giggs, and Gary Neville redefining loyalty.

Manchester United also has a history of breeding and attracting the best legs in the game. The club has maintained an incredible record of including at least one academy graduate in every matchday squad since 1937, a whooping 84 years and more than 4,100 games ago.

Duncan Edward, George Best, David Beckham, and Paul Scholes may have given way to Mason Greenwood, Shola Shoretire, Paul Pogba, and Marcus Rashford, but the Mancunians will never abandon their youth-centric policy. If you are good enough, then you will always be old enough. And that just keeps the fans wildly glued to their television and phone screens, ready to welcome the next star of the future!

Ballon d' Ors, FIFA World Player of the Year plaques, and hundreds of individual awards have made the trip to Old Trafford. Knights, bombs, slices of Pizza flying

in the tunnel, Kung Fu kicks, furious bust-ups, hard tackles, mesmerizing dribbles, shocking exits, dramatic transfers, smashed world transfer records, enigmatic individuals, and improbable comebacks all form a part of the club's history.

...And this book will guide you through all that history and a bit more. This book will provide you with tidbits and details of the origins, yesteryears, current state, and the prospects of Manchester United Football Club.

From its humble beginning as Newton Heath LYR FC, the club has grown to become an indomitable force in world football, and you deserve to know everything about its journey.

As you might imagine, there is a lot of information to cover. To help, that is why I have organized this book into 12 chapters. Each chapter will cover a unique aspect of the club, like its captains, stadium, legends, and titles. Each chapter will explore its subject in 20 trivia questions (with answers) and 10 mind-blowing fun facts. I know you may have devoted a healthy chunk of time to following the club, but I bet even you aren't prepared for some of the shocking facts we will uncover.

If you are a Manchester United fan or just interested in knowing more about this club, it is time to get strapped in for this ride about the men and circumstances that have made the Red Devils a household darling from New York City to New Delhi.

How much exactly do you know about Manchester United?

Do you really know why the Red Devils legends stand tall above everyone else?

Would you like to be able to ace any quiz about Manchester United?

Do you want to play trivia quiz games with fellow supporters, friends, or cousins?

If you have answered "Yes" to any of these questions, then I have written this book for your pleasure, education, and enjoyment.

This is your chance to finally stick one over that know-all guy in the pub who likes to reel out stats about your favourite club.

Dramatic comebacks are woven into the club's fabric; exciting players line up each season to thrill the fans, and there is always a buzz when the Red Devils take to the pitch.

You can now finally and properly key into that thrill and understand the things that make Manchester United tick, season after season after season.

Glory Glory, Man United!

ORIGIN

"It's a special club. It's got history. When I slip on the Manchester United shirt, it's like I'm wearing its past. So, you have to sacrifice yourself for this club."

-Patrice Evra

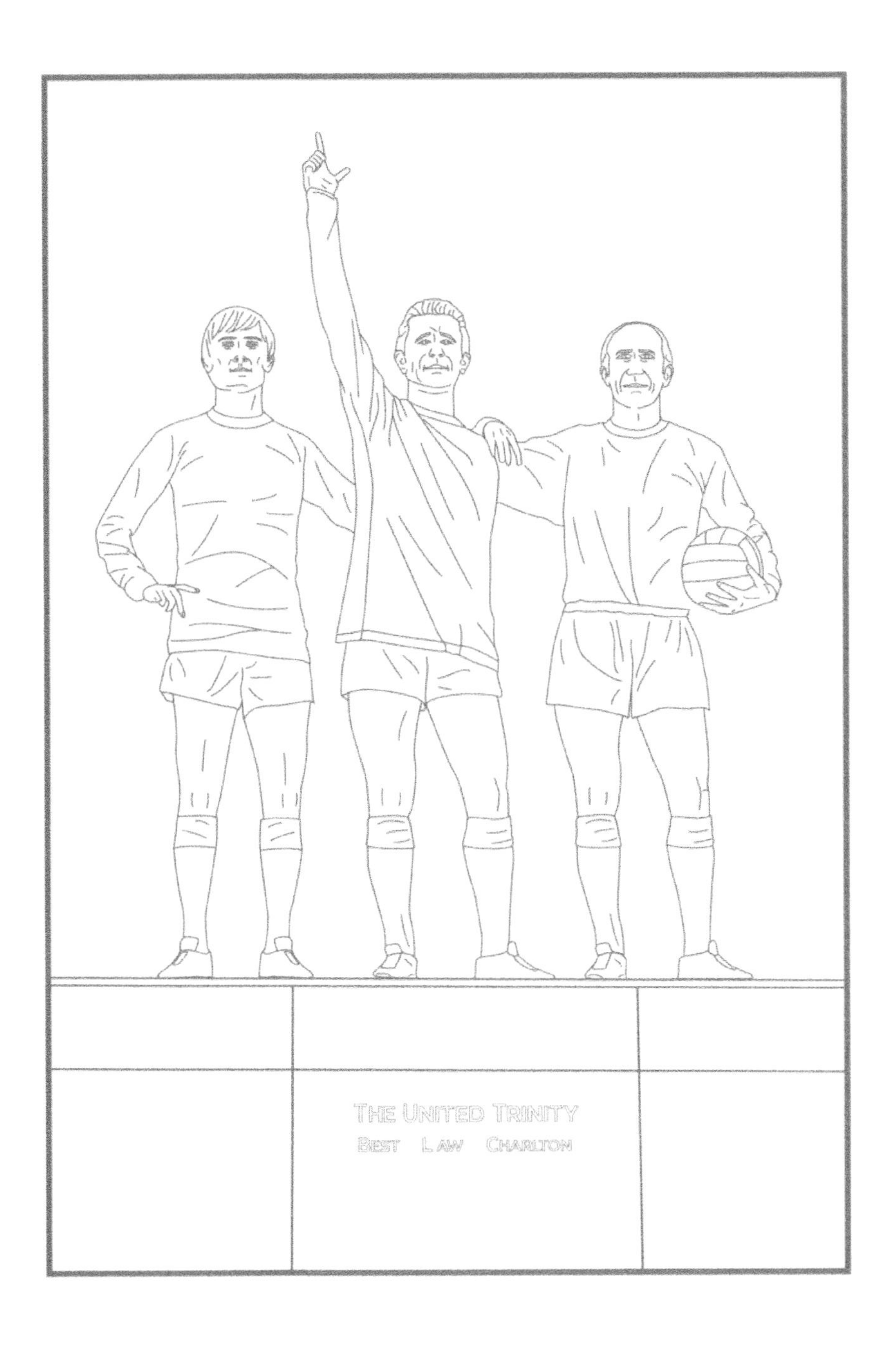
THE UNITED TRINITY
BEST LAW CHARLTON

20 Trivia Questions

1. In what year was Manchester United established?

   A. 1898

   B. 1878

   C. 1868

   D. 1858

2. At inception, by what name was the club "Manchester United" known?

   A. Newton Health LYR

   B. Manchester Central

   C. Busby United

   D. City of Manchester

   E.

3. What year did Manchester United join the English league?

   A. 1918

   B. 1892

   C. 1878

   D. 1888

4. In what year was Manchester United first relegated?

    A. 1894

    B. 1888

    C. 1868

    D. 1890

5. What year was the club rechristened as "Manchester United"?

    A. 1892

    B. 1901

    C. 1902

    D. 1898

6. Before the club was renamed Manchester United, what other name was considered?

    A. Manchester Central

    B. Manchester Union

    C. City of Manchester

    D. Busby Boys

7. When did the Munich air disaster occur?

    A. February 1958

    B. March 1956

    C. April 1965

    D. April 1954

8. Which European team did United play against before the Munich air disaster?
   A. Red Star Belgrade
   B. Bayern Munich
   C. Borussia Dortmund
   D. Real Madrid

9. What was the last English team Manchester United played against before the Munich air disaster?
   A. Liverpool FC
   B. Fulham FC
   C. Birmingham City
   D. Arsenal FC.

10. Legend has it that Manchester United was on the verge of bankruptcy in the early 20th century but was saved by the investment of a local brewery owner. What was his name?
    A. Harry Stafford
    B. John Henry Davies
    C. Clarence Hilditch
    D. Ernest Magnall

11. Which team did Manchester United defeat 4:0 to win their first-ever Charity Shield in 1908?
    A. Leeds United
    B. Stoke City
    C. Queens Park Rangers
    D. Sheffield Wednesday

12. Which team did Manchester United play against in their first league match after WW1 in 1919?

    A. Norwich City

    B. Derby County

    C. Chelsea

    D. Tottenham Hotspurs

13. When did Manchester United get its first kit sponsorship deal? Who was the Sponsor?

    A. 2006, AIG

    B. 1992, Vodafone

    C. 1982, Sharp

    D. 1985, Thomas Cook

14. Who wrote the popular club anthem "Glory Glory Man United"?

    A. Frank Renshaw

    B. Adams Goldsmith

    C. Kennedy Franklin

    D. Smith Johnson

15. In what year was the Manchester United badge officially redesigned to incorporate the devil?

    A. 1996

    B. 1976

    C. 1978

    D. 1970

16. When was the last change made on the Manchester United badge?
    A. 2000
    B. 1997
    C. 1998
    D. 1999

17. What is the name of the club's official mascot?
    A. Fred, the Red Devil
    B. Fred, the Red
    C. Dave, the Red
    D. Fred, the Devil

18. What is the kit number of the club's official mascot?
    A. 56
    B. 54
    C. 55
    D. 57

19. How many lives were lost in the Munich air disaster?
    A. 18
    B. 20
    C. 27
    D. 23

20. Which two players were first referred to as babes by newspapers in the famous Busby Babes squad?

    A. Jakie Blanchflower and Roger Byrne

    B. Jimmy Delaney and Stan Pearson

    C. Johnny Morris and Mitten Charlie

    D. Duncan Edwards and Harry Gregg

1. B – 1878
2. A – Newton Health LYR
3. B – 1892
4. A – 1894
5. C – 1902
6. A – Manchester Central
7. A – February 1958
8. A – Red Star Belgrade
9. D – Arsenal
10. B – John Henry Davies
11. C – Queens Park Rangers
12. B – Derby County
13. C – 1982, Sharp
14. A – Frank Renshaw
15. D – 1970
16. C – 1998
17. B – Fred, the Red
18. C – 55
19. D – 23
20. A – Jackie Blanchflower and Roger Byrne

10 Fun Facts

1. Manchester United Football Club was created in 1878 as Newton Heath LYR (Lancashire and Yorkshire) Football Club. It was initially a footballing club for the workers of the Wagon and Carriage Department of Newton Heath railroad company, and the team played against similar clubs. The club's first recorded official competitive match was a 6-0 loss to Bolton Wanderers in 1880.

2. In 1888, the club became an official member of the Combination, a regional competition for clubs of similar stature. Following its dissolution a year later, the club joined the Football Alliance before merging with The Football League.

3. The club almost went bankrupt in 1902, but the captain, Harry Strafford, saved it by convincing 4 different local businessmen to invest £500 each, thereby clearing practically 80% of the £2,670 debt. In 2021 terms and adjusted for inflation, that figure would be about £290,000.

4. As part of the agreement for saving the club, the name was changed to Manchester United Football Club in the same year, and John Henry Davies became the club's president.

5. The club's original colours were green and gold, the official colours of the railway company. This was changed in 1928 to the famed red, black, and white colours, which have survived to date

6. In 1931, the club was again on the brink of bankruptcy, and again, a local businessman, James W. Gibson, stepped in with £2,000 to save the club.

7. The first great era in the history of Manchester United FC (some would argue even greater than the Fergie era) was created by Sir Matt Busby. Sir Busby built the famed Busby Babes, a young and exciting team that won the league with an average age of 22. The babes won 3 league titles in 6 years.

8. Tragedy struck in what is now known as the "Munich Air Disaster" on the 6th of February, 1958, when a plane carrying the squad went down in Munich shortly after refuelling. Twenty-three lives, including that of 8 players, were lost in the crash.

9. Sir Busby decided on the name "The Red Devils." The club's original nickname was "The Pagans" until the Busby Babes. After Sir Busby had to rebuild the team following the Munich crash, he borrowed the name "Red Devils" from a rugby team. The name has stuck till today.

10. The current owners, The Glazer family, bought the club in 2005 for $800 million in a leveraged deal that has seen widespread condemnation from fans for saddling the club with debt. Notable, coordinated protests against the Glazers' ownership feature the fans putting on the original green and gold colours of the club.

STADIUM

"I know the city and the club, and I can tell you that when you play for Manchester United at Old Trafford, you no longer need to see the sunshine every day."

-Patrice Evra

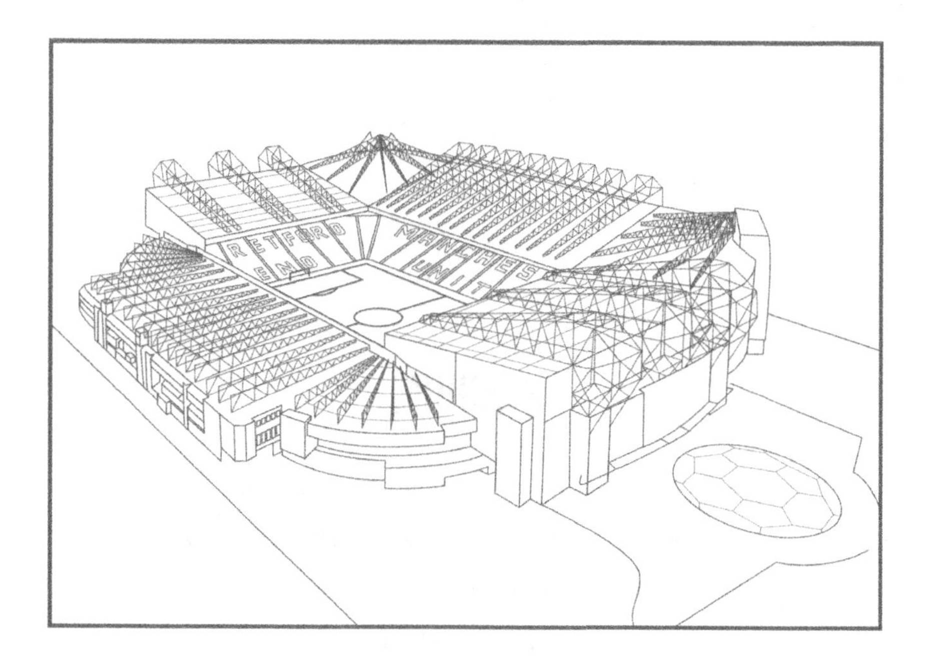

20 Trivia Questions

1. What was Manchester United's first stadium called?

   A. North Road

   B. Bank Road

   C. Railway Road

   D. Yorkshire Ground

2. In what year did Manchester United commence the construction of old Trafford?

   A. 1915

   B. 1910

   C. 1908

   D. 1907

3. Who was the supervising architect in the construction of Old Trafford?

   A. Archibald Leitch

   B. Sir Huges Elliot

   C. Alex Bell

   D. Jimmy Turnbull

4. Which team did Manchester United play against in the maiden match at Old Trafford?

    A. Bayern Munich

    B. Real Madrid

    C. Liverpool

    D. Juventus

5. What was the attendance at the maiden match at the Old Trafford stadium?

    A. 67,000

    B. 75,451

    C. 81,000

    D. 80,000

6. What year did Old Trafford welcome its first European opposition?

    A. 25th of April 1957

    B. 25th of April 1956

    C. 25th of April 1958

    D. 25th of April 1955

7. What is Old Trafford's record attendance in a single match?

    A. 80,000

    B. 76,962

    C. 74,684

    D. 75,234

8. Which match attracted Old Trafford's record attendance figure?

    A. Manchester United vs. Leeds United

    B. Manchester City vs. Southampton

    C. Wolverhampton Wanderers vs. Grimsby Town

    D. Manchester United vs. Real Madrid

9. When was Old Trafford bombed during the second world war?

    A. 11th of March, 1941

    B. 11th of March, 1940

    C. 11th of March, 1942

    D. 11th of March, 1939

10. The statue of George Best, Dennis Law, and Bobby Charlton at Old Trafford is known as?

    A. The Legends of United

    B. The United Trinity

    C. The Trinity Heroes

    D. The Heroes of United

11. What is Old Trafford affectionately known as?

    A. Red Bricks

    B. The Theater of Dreams

    C. The Devils Lair

    D. The Banks Street

12. Two stands at Old Trafford are named after two legends. What are their names?

    A. Sir Mathew Busby and Jimmy Murphy

    B. Sir Alex Ferguson and Ernest Mangall

    C. Sir Alex Ferguson and Sir Mathew Busby

    D. Sir Alex Ferguson and Stan Pearson

13. What is the highest winning margin in a Premier League match at Old Trafford?

    A. 8:2

    B. 10:1

    C. 9:0

    D. 8:1

14. What was Manchester's United highest attendance at Old Trafford stadium as an all-seater stadium?

    A. 76,098

    B. 75,640

    C. 75,000

    D. 75,234

15. What was the scoreline of Manchester United's heaviest defeat in the Premier League era at Old Trafford?

    A. 1:7

    B. 2:8

    C. 1:6

    D. 0:8

16. Which teams inflicted the heaviest defeat on Manchester United at Old Trafford in the premier league era?

    A. Chelsea and Manchester City

    B. Liverpool and Manchester City

    C. Manchester City and Leeds United

    D. Tottenham Hotspur and Manchester City

17. What is Manchester United's longest unbeaten run in the Premier League era at Old Trafford?

    A. 38

    B. 36

    C. 42

    D. 40

18. What was the scoreline of Manchester United's highest win at home ever?

    A. 9:1

    B. 9:0

    C. 10:0

    D. 11:0

19. What is the measurement of the pitch at Old Trafford?

    A. 108m x 63m

    B. 105m x 68m

    C. 103m x 65m

    D. 106m x 64m

20. When did Old Trafford host the Champions League final?

    A. 2003

    B. 2002

    C. 1997

    D. 1998

20 Trivia Answers

1. A – North Road
2. C – 1908
3. A – Archibald Leitch
4. C – Liverpool
5. D – 80,000
6. A – the 25th of April 1957
7. B – 76,962
8. C– Wolverhampton Wanderers vs. Grimsby Town
9. A – the 11th of March, 1941
10. B – The United Trinity
11. B – Theater of Dreams
12. C – Sir Alex Ferguson and Sir Mathew Busby
13. C – 9:0
14. A – 76,098
15. C – 1:6
16. D – Tottenham Hotspur and Manchester City
17. B – 36
18. C – 10:0
19. B – 105m x 68m
20. A – 2003

10 Fun Facts

1. Old Trafford was not the original home of The Red Devils. They first played at North Road (with a capacity of 12,000 fans) until 1893 and Bank Street Football Ground (with a capacity of 50,000 fans) until 1910.
2. The original intention for Old Trafford was to build a stadium with a capacity to hold 100,000 fans, but this had to be scaled back due to financial and safety concerns. The architect for the construction was Archibald Leitch, who is famous for having designed several other stadia. Messrs. Brameld and Smith handled the construction. The inaugural match at Old Trafford was a 4-3 defeat to Liverpool in February of 1910.
3. Old Trafford has four all-seater stands; the East (The Scoreboard End), West (Stretford End), North (Sir Alex Ferguson stand), and South (Sir Bobby Charlton) stands. The North stand can hold 26,000 spectators, the most of all four stands, but the most famous stand is the Stretford End, where the most diehard fans are located. It is also reputed to create the loudest noise among all the stands. The East stand was the location of the scoreboard and features seats for disabled supporters.
4. Old Trafford was nearly destroyed by German bombing during World War 2. This was because it was near industrial zones and was often used by the military for several functions. After WW2, the rebuild of Old Trafford took 8 years, from 1941 to 1949. During that period, The Red Devils had to play in a stadium called Maine Road, which belonged to city rivals, Manchester City FC.
5. With 74,140 seats, Old Trafford is the second biggest stadium in England, second only to Wembley Stadium. Across Europe, it is the eleventh largest stadium and pulls mammoth attendance records.
6. The record attendance figure in a match at Old Trafford during the Premier League era is 76,098 in a 2007 match against Blackburn Rovers. In 1939,

though, the stadium recorded its highest attendance when 76,962 spectators watched the FA cup semi-final between Grimsby Town and Wolverhampton Wanderers.

7. Old Trafford hosted the final of the UEFA Champions League in 2003 between Italian giants, AC Milan and Juventus. That is the only UCL final it has hosted. It has also hosted 3 FA Cup finals and matches in the 1966 World Cup, Euro 96, and the 2012 Olympics.
8. During the rebuild of the new Wembley Stadium, the England National team played its home matches across different stadia. Between 2003 to 2007, Old Trafford hosted 12 of the national team's 23 home matches, the most for any stadium.
9. The biggest attractions at Old Trafford include the statues of two legendary managers, Sir Alex Ferguson and Sir Matt Busby, and The Holy Trinity statue of George Best, Denis Law, and Sir Bobby Charlton.
10. The pitch at Old Trafford measures 105m by 68m. The pitch is about 9 inches higher than the surrounding edges to ease surface water drainage. The pitch also has a heating system 10m under the pitch that consists of 37km of plastic pipes.

MANAGERS

"I had to lift players' expectations. They should never give in. I said that to them all the time: "If you give in once, you'll give in twice."

-Sir Alex Ferguson

20 Trivia Questions

1. __________ was appointed as the club secretary in September 1903 and is widely considered as the club's first manager.
   A. Harry Strafford
   B. Ernest Mangnall
   C. J. J. Bentley
   D. John Robson

2. What year was Sir Mathew Busby appointed as Manchester United's Manager?
   A. 1952
   B. 1947
   C. 1943
   D. 1945

3. Who was Sir Mathew Busby's assistant and righthand man?
   A. Jimmy Murphy
   B. John Robson
   C. Harry Strafford
   D. Matt Murphy

4. What league position did United finish in in Sir Mathew Busby's first season in charge as the manager?

   A. Third

   B. Second

   C. Seventh

   D. Fifth

5. What was the first trophy won by Sir Mathew Busby as United's Manager?

   A. The Charity Shield

   B. The FA Cup

   C. The League Championship

   D. The Community Shield

6. What was Sir Mathew Busby's nationality?

   A. Irish

   B. Welsh

   C. English

   D. Scottish

7. From which club did Sir Alex Ferguson join Manchester United?

   A. Celtic

   B. Rangers

   C. Aberdeen

   D. Queens Park Rangers

8. Who was the manager when Manchester United was relegated in the 1973/1974 season?

   A. Wilf McGuinness

   B. Tommy Docherty

   C. Sir Matt Busby

   D. Jimmy Murphy

9. How long was Dave Sexton's reign as United manager?

   A. 3 years

   B. 6 years

   C. 4 years

   D. 1 year

10. How long was Sir Mathew Busby's reign as Manchester United's manager?

    A. 25 years

    B. 28 years

    C. 26 years

    D. 30 years

11. Which coach took over from Sir Mathew Busby?

    A. Wilf McGuinness

    B. Jimmy Murphy

    C. Dave Sexton

    D. Frank O'Farrell

12. Who is the shortest-serving full-time Manchester United manager (Not Caretaker)?

    A. Jimmy Murphy

    B. Walter Crickmer

    C. T. J Wallworth

    D. John Chapman

13. Who was the first Scot to manage Manchester United?

    A. John Chapman

    B. Matthew Busby

    C. Tommy Docherty

    D. Scott Duncan

14. Who is widely considered the second most successful Manchester United Manager?

    A. John Chapman

    B. Sir Mathew Busby

    C. Scott Duncan

    D. Ron Atkinson

15. How many Scottish managers have Manchester United had?

    A. 5

    B. 4

    C. 3

    D. 6

16. Which player was Sir Alex Ferguson's record signing as Manchester United's manager?

    A. Wayne Rooney

    B. Juan Sebastian Veron

    C. Rio Ferdinand

    D. Dimitar Berbatov

17. How many matches did Sir Alex Ferguson oversee as the manager?

    A. 1600

    B. 1210

    C. 1500

    D. 1450

18. In his second stint as United's manager, how many games did Sir Mathew Busby manage?

    A. 21

    B. 11

    C. 15

    D. 31

19. In his first season as Manchester United manager, what league position did Sir Alex Ferguson's side finish in?

    A. Eleventh

    B. Seventh

    C. Ninth

    D. Third

20. Who was the opponent in Sir Alex Ferguson's last game in charge of Manchester United?

    A. Newcastle United

    B. West Brom

    C. Norwich City

    D. Blackburn Rovers

20 Trivia Answers

1. **B – Ernest Mangnall**
2. **D – 1945**
3. **A – Jimmy Murphy**
4. **B – Second**
5. **B – The FA Cup**
6. **D – Scottish**
7. **C – Aberdeen**
8. **B – Tommy Docherty**
9. **C – 4 Years**
10. **A – 25 Years**
11. **A – Wilf McGuiness**
12. **C – T. J. Wallworth**
13. **A – John Chapman**
14. **B – Sir Mathew Busby**
15. **D – 6**
16. **C – Rio Ferdinand**
17. **C – 1500**
18. **A – 21**
19. **A – Eleventh**
20. **B – West Brom**

10 Fun Facts

1. Ernest Mangnall was the first manager to win silverware for Manchester United. Under him, the club won its first Football League title in 1908. He also won the FA Cup and another league title with the Red Devils. However, he left to join city rivals, Manchester City, in 1912. His last match in charge of the Red Devils was the Old Trafford Derby in September 2012.

2. Sir Matt Busby oversaw a period of dominance for the Red Devils in England. He was first appointed the manager in October 1945 after the club promised him more control than Liverpool was willing to offer him as a potential manager. He only won his first league title in 1952 and is credited with blooding numerous youth talents at the club. The core of his youthful team became known as the Busby Babes. He won 5 First Division titles, 2 FA Cups, 5 Charity Shields, and 1 European Cup during his reign.

3. Manchester United has had 7 managers in the Premier League era. Only Sir Alex Ferguson has won the Premier League for the club. He is also the only English manager to have won a treble – the league title, the Champions League, and FA Cup in the same season. He won the treble in the 1998/1999 season and was knighted by the Queen for his achievements.

4. Sir Alex Ferguson is also the most decorated manager in the club's history, with 38 trophies at Manchester United. This is in addition to the 8 titles he had won elsewhere before joining Manchester United.

5. Sir Alex Ferguson was the club's manager for 27 years (1986-2013). He was also the manager for the first 21 Premier League seasons. Upon his retirement, he was the longest-serving coach not just in the English top-flight but across the top 5 European leagues.

6. Upon his retirement, Sir Alex had won the most points (1,752), most matches (410), most manager of the month awards (27), and most manager of the season awards in the Premier League. He had also won the most Premier

League trophies (13) as a manager.

7. During his reign as the boss, Sir Alex won 13 Premier League titles, 5 FA Cups, 4 League Cups, 10 Community Shields, 2 Champions League titles, 1 European Cup Winners' Cup, 1 European Super Cup, 1 Intercontinental Cup, and 1 FIFA Club World Cup.

8. Ole Gunnar Solskjaer was the first former player to be appointed as full-term manager at Manchester United. He was initially appointed as a caretaker manager, but after a string of impressive performances, he was offered a permanent deal until his sack in 2021 after a poor run. He left the club as the first full-time manager since Frank O'Farrell, not to win a trophy for the club.

9. Louis Van Gaal was appointed as the club's first non-British manager on the 19th of May, 2014. Under him, the club returned to the UEFA Champions League and won the 2016 FA cup, but he was sacked after two seasons in charge and replaced by the Portuguese, Jose Mourinho.

10. In the Premier League era, Jose Mourinho is the club's second-most decorated manager. He won 3 titles – 1 Europa league, 1 league cup, and 1 community shield trophy, but dressing room unrest and queries about his tactics led to his sack.

GOALIES

"In football, you sometimes have beauty and cruelty together."

-Peter Schmeichel

20 Trivia Questions

1. How many leagues appearance did Victor Valdes manage for Manchester United?

   A. 10

   B. 15

   C. 3

   D. 2

2. At what age did David De Gea join Manchester United?

   A. 18

   B. 20

   C. 17

   D. 19

3. What is the total number of record consecutive clean sheets kept by Edwin Van Der Sar for Manchester United?

   A. 12

   B. 13

   C. 10

   D. 14

4. From which premier league club was Edwin Van Der Sar signed?

   A. West Brom

   B. West Ham

   C. Fulham

   D. Aston Villa

5. Which goalkeeper holds the record for the highest number of appearances for Manchester United?

   A. David De Gea

   B. Edwin Van Der Sa

   C. Peter Schmeichel

   D. Alexander Stepney

6. Which club did Manchester United sign Peter Schmeichel from?

   A. Hvidovre

   B. Brondby

   C. Sporting CP

   D. Aston Villa

7. Which club did Fabian Barthez join after leaving Manchester United?

   A. Monaco

   B. Marseille

   C. Toulouse

   D. Nantes

8. Which French club was Fabian Barthez signed from?
    A. Monaco
    B. Toulouse
    C. Nantes
    D. Marseille

9. What is the longest run of consecutive clean sheets kept by a Manchester United goalkeeper?
    A. 14
    B. 15
    C. 17
    D. 12

10. Who was the first Scottish Manchester United goalkeeper?
    A. Francis Barrett
    B. Andy Goram
    C. Jim Leighton
    D. Arthur Lochhead

11. Who was the first Spanish Manchester United goalkeeper?
    A. David De Gea
    B. Victor Valdes
    C. Ricardo
    D. Arnua Puigmal

12. What is the highest number of saves in a single Premier League match by David De Gea at Manchester United?

    A. 12

    B. 10

    C. 14

    D. 15

13. In which competition did Peter Schmeichel play his last match as a Manchester United goalkeeper?

    A. The FA Cup

    B. The Champions League

    C. The Premier League

    D. The Club World Cup

14. Which Manchester United's keeper is regarded as the Hero of Munich?

    A. Peter Schmeichel

    B. Edwin Van Der Sar

    C. Harry Gregg

    D. Jim Leighton

15. At what age did Manchester United sign Edwin Van Der Sar?

    A. 38

    B. 36

    C. 32

    D. 34

16. Who was the first Manchester United goalkeeper to win the Sir Mathew Busby "player of the year" award?

    A. Harry Gregg

    B. Edwin Van Der Sar

    C. Peter Schmeichel

    D. David De Gea

17. Who is the oldest goalkeeper to play for Manchester United?

    A. Edwin Van Der Sar

    B. Jim Leighton

    C. Peter Schmeichel

    D. Francis Barrett

18. How many goalkeepers have scored a goal for Manchester United?

    A. 6

    B. 5

    C. 4

    D. 2

19. In his first season as United's keeper, what was David De Gea's squad number?

    A. 19

    B. 14

    C. 12

    D. 1

20. Which Manchester United keeper has the most goals for the club?

    A. Alex Stepney

    B. David De Gea

    C. Edwin Van Der Sar

    D. Peter Schmeichel

20 Trivia Answers

1. D – 2
2. D – 19
3. D – 14
4. C – Fulham
5. C – Peter Schmeichel
6. B – Brondby
7. B – Marseille
8. A – Monaco
9. A – 14
10. A – Francis Barrett
11. C – Ricardo
12. C – 14
13. B – The Champions League
14. C – Harry Gregg
15. D – 34
16. D – David De Gea
17. A – Edwin Van Der Sar
18. D – 2
19. D – 1
20. A – Alex Stepney

10 Fun Facts

1. Alex Stepney was the first Manchester United goalkeeper to score for the club. In the 1973/1974 season, he scored two penalties to become the club's joint leading goalscorer at Christmas. That highlights how terrible that campaign was for Manchester United, and the club got relegated at the end of the season.
2. Peter Schmeichel is the only Manchester United goalkeeper to have scored from open play. He achieved this feat against Rotor Vologr069 in a 1995 UEFA cup tie. At the time, the goal helped to protect the club's 40-year unbeaten home record. Schmeichel also became the first goalkeeper to score in the Premier League when he netted for Aston Villa against Everton.
3. Peter Schmeichel is considered the most successful keeper, winning 15 trophies, including 5 Premier League and a UEFA Champions League title. He also recorded 180 clean sheets (a staggering 42% of all games he played for the club), with 112 in the EPL alone. He hit double-figures for clean sheets in all his seasons at Man United, with the highest number in the 1994/95 season (22 in 33 games).

4. After Schmeichel left Manchester United, the club tried unsuccessfully to replace him. Mark Bosnich, Massimo Taibi, Fabian Barthez, Tim Howard, and Roy Carroll all tried unsuccessfully to replicate his presence and skills.

5. Edwin Van der Sar finally filled the Schmeichel void in goal after he was signed from Fulham in 2005. He recorded a total of 90 clean sheets for Manchester United and a career total of 132 clean sheets.

6. In January 2009, Van der Sar broke the Premier League record for consecutive clean sheets after helping Manchester United to a 5-0 win over West Bromwich Albion. That win took him to 1,032 minutes without conceding. In the next game week, he then broke the all-time English League record of 1,103 for consecutive minutes without conceding a goal. He then broke the British top-flight record of 1,155 minutes against West Ham. And finally, he extended his record to 1,302 minutes to break the world record of 1,289 minutes. Peter Lovenkrands of Newcastle United finally broke through Van der Sar's goal to end this impressive run at 1,311 minutes.

7. At 40 years, 211 days, Edwin Van der Sar became the oldest player to feature in a UEFA Champions League final, when Manchester United lost 3-1 to Barcelona in the 2011 final. This game was also incidentally his last game for Manchester United as he retired after the match.

8. David de Gea has been crowned the club's player of the season 4 times. That is more than any other player, and he won three of these titles in a row. He is also the longest-serving club number one (in the Premier League era) at 10 years with 354 appearances and 125 clean sheets.

9. The flamboyant Fabien Barthez once played for Man United as a winger. It was in a friendly match and he came on as a substitute, but he more than held his own. His first move was a cool nutmeg.

10. In total, Manchester United goalkeepers have made 893 saves (with 474 clean sheets) and conceded 1,033 goals in the Premier League era.

DEFENDERS

"No matter how much silverware you win in your career, you always want more."

-Nemanja Vidic

20 Trivia Questions

1. Which defender has the highest number of goals for Manchester United?

    A. Harry Maguire

    B. Steve Bruce

    C. Lauren Blanc

    D. Nemanja Vidic

2. Which defender holds the record for the highest number of appearances for Manchester United in the Premier League?

    A. Steve Bruce

    B. Nemanja Vidic

    C. Gary Neville

    D. Rio Ferdinand

3. Who was the first Brazilian fullback to play for Manchester United in the Premier League?

    A. Sergio Da Silva

    B. Fabio Pereira Da Silva

    C. Rafael Pereira Da Silva

    D. Alex Telles

4. Which defender has the highest number of red cards for Manchester United in the Premier League?

   A. Gary Neville

   B. Rio Ferdinand

   C. Patrice Evra

   D. Nemanja Vidic

5. Who holds the record for the highest number of yellow cards for Manchester United among defenders?

   A. Rio Ferdinand

   B. Gary Neville

   C. Phil Neville

   D. Nemanja Vidic

6. In what year did Manchester United sign the defensive duo of Nemanja Vidic and Patrice Evra?

   A. 2004

   B. 2006

   C. 2005

   D. 2008

7. Which Manchester United defender has conceded the most own goals?

   A. Wes Brown

   B. Mark Jones

   C. Phil Jones

   D. Billy Foulkes

8. Which Manchester United defender holds the record for the third-highest appearances for Manchester United?

   A. Roger Bryne

   B. Gary Neville

   C. Billy Foulkes

   D. Rio Ferdinand

9. Which of these pairs has served as a goalkeeper when needed?

   A. Rio Ferdinand and John O'Shea

   B. Rio Ferdinand and Gary Neville

   C. John O'Shea and Phil Neville

   D. Rio Ferdinand and Phil Jones

10. Who is the most expensive Manchester United defender of all time?

    A. Rio Ferdinand

    B. Harry Maguire

    C. Aaron Wan Bissaka

    D. Jaap Stam

11. Who holds the record for the highest number of assists among Manchester United Defenders in the Premier League era?

    A. Gary Pallister

    B. Patrice Evra

    C. Gary Neville

    D. Nemanja Vidic

12. Who is the oldest defender to score a goal for Manchester United?

    A. Laurent Blanc

    B. Gary Neville

    C. Rio Ferdinand

    D. Harry Maguire

13. Who was the first French defender to play for Manchester United?

    A. Laurent Blanc

    B. Patrice Evra

    C. Mikael Silvestre

    D. William Prunier

14. Which Manchester United defender has the highest number of goals for the England National Team?

    A. Rio Ferdinand

    B. Gary Neville

    C. Phil Neville

    D. Harry Maguire

15. Which of these defenders played both as a right-back and left-back regularly?

    A. Gary Neville

    B. Dennis Irwin

    C. Patrice Evra

    D. Phil Jones

16. Who is the most substituted-off Manchester United defender in the Premier League?

    A. Denis Irwin

    B. Gary Neville

    C. John O'Shea

    D. Phil Neville

17. Who is the youngest-ever defender to score a goal at Manchester United?

    A. David Sadler

    B. Gary Neville

    C. Timothy Fosu Mensah

    D. Fabio Da Silva

18. Who is the oldest defender to ever feature for Manchester United?

    A. Gary Neville

    B. Bill Foulkes

    C. Nemanja Vidic

    D. Laurent Blanc

19. Who holds the record for the youngest ever defender to make a debut for Manchester United in the Premier League?

    A. Rafael Da Silva

    B. Timothy Fosu Mensah

    C. Phil Neville

    D. Gerard Pique

20. Who is the record goalscoring defender for Manchester United in the Premier League era?

    A. Steve Bruce

    B. Nemanja Vidic

    C. Rio Ferdinand

    D. Jimmy Bradford

20 Trivia Answers

1. B – Steve Bruce
2. C – Gary Neville
3. C – Rafael Pereira Da Silva
4. D – Nemanja Vidic
5. B – Gary Neville
6. B – 2006
7. D – Billy Foulkes
8. C – Billy Foulkes
9. A - Rio Ferdinand and John O'Shea
10. B – Maguire
11. C – Gary Neville
12. A – Laurent Blanc
13. D – William Prunier
14. D – Harry Maguire
15. B – Dennis Irwin
16. A – Dennis Irwin
17. A – David Sadler
18. B – Bill Foulkes
19. D – Gerard Pique
20. A – Steve Bruce

10 Fun Facts

1. Roger Bryne was Manchester United's captain at the time of the Munich air disaster and lost his life to the crash. He died at 28 years old and had 245 appearances for United.
2. Bill Foulkes is the defender with the highest number of appearances for the club. He turned out for the Red Devils, a record 688 times, and scored 9 goals in 18 seasons. He also replaced Roger Bryne as the club captain after the Munich disaster
3. The Nemanja Vidic - Rio Ferdinand is one of the best partnerships in Premier League history. They started 187 games together and kept 91 clean sheets.
4. Steve Bruce is the defender with the highest number of goals for Manchester United. Signed for only 825,000 Euros, Bruce played 414 times for Manchester United and scored 51 goals.
5. Dennis Irwin featured as a left-back for Manchester United for 12 years. In this time, he scored 33 goals and provided 23 assists for Manchester United in a glittering career that featured league and continental success. He also regularly appeared as a right-back and was noted for great skills and delivery from set-piece situations.
6. In the 2008/2009 season, Nemanja Vidic scored 8 goals in a single season. The only squad members who had more for that season were Rooney, Tevez, and Ronaldo.
7. Gary Neville spent 20 years at Old Trafford, winning 31 trophies, including 12 EPL, 4 FA cup, 2 UEFA Champions League, 2 World Club Cup, and 8 Community Shield titles. He is the most decorated Manchester United defender of all time.
8. In 4 years at Old Trafford, Gerard Pique only made 12 appearances. However, he joined Barcelona and has gone on to win every trophy on offer.

9. Jaap Stam, the Dutch centre-back spent three seasons at Manchester United and won the league in all of them as a pivotal member of the squad. He was, however, sold to Lazio in 2001. Reports at the time suggested that this was because he had upset Sir Alex Ferguson with certain claims he made in his autobiography *Head to Head.*

10. Harry Maguire, the current captain, is the most expensive defender in the game's history. Manchester United paid a reported 85m pounds fee to Leicester City to secure his signature. Harry Maguire is also England's highest-scoring defender of all time with 7 goals. Six of these goals have come via headers.

MIDFIELDERS

"I don't like compliments. No. I prefer criticism; prefer to prove them wrong."

-Paul Scholes

20 Trivia Questions

1. Which Manchester United midfielder holds the record for most assists?

   A. Paul Scholes

   B. Ryan Giggs

   C. Eric Cantona

   D. Roy Keane

2. Which Manchester United midfielder holds the record for most goals in the Premier League?

   A. Nani

   B. Paul Scholes

   C. Ryan Giggs

   D. Michael Carrick

3. Who holds the record for the highest number of red cards for Manchester United among midfielders in the Premier League?

   A. Eric Cantona

   B. Roy Keane

   C. Paul Scholes

   D. Paul Pogba

4. Who holds the record for the highest number of yellow cards for Manchester United among midfielders in the Premier League?

   A. Paul Scholes

   B. Roy Keane

   C. Darren Fletcher

   D. Ryan Giggs

5. Who was the first Brazilian midfielder to play for Manchester United?

   A. Rodrigo Possebon

   B. Bebe

   C. Anderson

   D. Kleberson

6. Who is the most expensive midfield signing of all time at Manchester United?

   A. Paul Scholes

   B. Paul Pogba

   C. Bruno Fernandes

   D. Juan Sebastian Veron

7. Who is the only Russian to have played for Manchester United?

   A. Alexsei Miranchuk

   B. Andrey Kanchelskis

   C. Sergie Petrov

   D. Anton Miranchuk

8. Which of these former Manchester United midfielders is not English?

   A. Michael Carrick

   B. Ryan Giggs

   C. Paul Scholes

   D. Alan Smith

9. Which of these Manchester United midfielders has the highest number of appearances for the club?

   A. Paul Scholes

   B. Michael Carrick

   C. Roy Keane

   D. Ryan Giggs

10. What is the record number of appearances for a Manchester United midfielder?

    A. 752

    B. 867

    C. 941

    D. 1100

11. Who is the oldest midfielder to play for Manchester United in the Premier League?

    A. Ryan Giggs

    B. Darren Fletcher

    C. Roy Keane

    D. Shay Brennon

12. Who is the youngest ever midfielder to play for Manchester United in the Premier League?

    A. Angel Gomes

    B. Shola Shoretire

    C. Nicky Butt

    D. Phil Neville

13. Who is the Scottish midfielder with the most appearances for Manchester United?

    A. Liam Miller

    B. Mick Martin

    C. Roy Keane

    D. Ashley Grimes

14. Which of these midfielders did Sir Alex want to take the number 7 jersey before David Beckham took it?

    A. Roy Keane

    B. Ryan Giggs

    C. Nicky Butt

    D. Paul Scholes

15. Which Portuguese club sold Bruno Fernandes, Nani, and Cristiano Ronaldo to Manchester United?

    A. Porto

    B. Sporting C.P

    C. Boavista

    D. Benfica

16. Which club does former Manchester United midfielder, Tom Cleverley, appear for in the 2021/2022 season?

    A. Brentford F.C
    B. Watford F. C
    C. Wolverhampton Wanderers
    D. Newcastle United

17. How many Brazilians have played for Manchester United?

    A. 5
    B. 6
    C. 7
    D. 8

18. Which midfielder has taken the most penalties for Manchester United in the Premier League?

    A. Paul Scholes
    B. Roy Keane
    C. Bruno Fernandes
    D. Paul Pogba

19. Which of these clubs did Anderson make his competitive debut against?

    A. Sunderland FC
    B. Portsmouth FC
    C. Bolton Wanderers
    D. Arsenal FC.

20. Who is fondly referred to as *El Magnifico* by Manchester United fans?

    A. Anderson

    B. Paul Scholes

    C. Bruno Fernandes

    D. Juan Sebastian Veron

20 Trivia Answers

1. B – Ryan Giggs
2. C – Ryan Giggs
3. B – Roy Keane
4. A – Paul Scholes
5. D – Kleberson
6. B – Paul Pogba
7. B – Andrey Kanchelskis
8. B – Ryan Giggs
9. D - Ryan Giggs
10. C – 941
11. A – Ryan Giggs
12. A – Angel Gomes
13. C – Roy Keane
14. A – Roy Keane
15. B – Sporting CP
16. B – Watford F.C
17. C – 7
18. C – Bruno Fernandes
19. A – Sunderland FC
20. C – Bruno Fernandes

10 Fun Facts

1. David Beckham starred for Manchester United for 13 years. During this time, he scored 85 goals in 394 appearances and became the poster boy of the Premier League. Affectionately referred to as "The Golden Boy," he was the first superstar football celebrity. But his newfound commitments away from the pitch after he got married did not sit entirely well with Sir Alex Ferguson, and that led to his eventual exit in 2003.
2. No Premier League player has recorded more free-kick goals than David Beckham. He scored 18 free-kicks as a Manchester United player in the PL That is 6 more goals than the players with the second-highest figure – Gianfranco Zola and Thierry Henry with 12 goals. His last goal for Manchester United was also a free-kick vs. Everton.
3. Roy Keane picked up the highest number of red cards for a Manchester United player, 11, just 2 more than Paul Scholes. He holds the record for the highest number of red cards in English Football history, with 13 red cards. He was inducted into the English Football Hall of Fame in 2004.
4. David Beckham met his future wife, Victoria, of the *Spice Girls* fame, in the United players' lounge after a charity match in 1997. The duo became a power couple and got married in an event that cost 698,000 pounds. He has *99* tattooed on his finger in tribute to the year 1999. That was the year he married Victoria, had his first son, Brooklyn, and helped United win the treble.
5. Ryan Giggs was the only player to appear in the first 22 seasons of the Premier League. He was also the only player to score in the first 21 seasons. He also holds medals for each of Manchester United's Premier League 13 titles.
6. Ryan Giggs finished with 963 appearances (the most for Manchester United) and 168 goals. In his 24 seasons at Manchester United, he never received a red card.

7. Paul Scholes is Manchester United's third-highest appearance maker with 718 appearances and 155 goals. He also made 66 appearances for England and scored 14 goals.

8. In the Premier League era, Manchester United has twice broken the British transfer record to sign midfielders Juan Sebastian Veron and Paul Pogba.

9. Following a midfield injury crisis in January 2012, Paul Scholes came out of retirement to rejoin the Manchester United team. Scholes had earlier retired on the 31st of May 2011. He donned the number 22 jersey upon his return since his erstwhile number 18 had been given to Ashley Young. In his first start after his comeback, he scored against Bolton Wanderers from a Wayne Rooney assist. He went on to sign a one-year extension with Manchester United until the end of the 2013 season, when he retired for the second and final time.

10. Paul Scholes was noted for his bad tackles almost as well as his passing range and playmaking ability. He received a club-high 97 yellow cards and 4 red cards in his Premier League career. Upon his retirement, only two players had more yellow cards across the whole league.

FORWARDS

"At United, there are great traditions, which you can't buy in one or two years. They are created by victories. You need to prove again and again that you are better than the others. Manchester United have always done this, and are still doing it, so they are the best."

-Cristiano Ronaldo

20 Trivia Questions

1. Which Manchester United forward is the all-time goalscorer for the club?

   A. Sir Bobby Charlton

   B. George Best

   C. Wayne Rooney

   D. Ruud van Nistelrooy

2. Who scored a famous stoppage-time goal to win the UCL in 1999?

   A. Dwight Yorke

   B. Eric Cantona

   C. Teddy Sheringham

   D. Ole Gunnar Solskjaer

3. In the Premier League match between Manchester United and Nottingham Forest in 1999, who scored four goals in 13 minutes?

   A. Teddy Sheringham

   B. Ole Gunnar Solskjaer

   C. Dwight Yorke

   D. David Healy

4. How many Premier League hattricks did Eric Cantona score for Manchester United?

   A. 6

   B. 4

   C. 2

   D. None

5. Which former Manchester United forward is nicknamed 'Chicharito'?

   A. Bobby Charlton

   B. Javier Hernandez

   C. Eric Cantona

   D. Robin van Persie

6. Which country does the Manchester United forward nicknamed *El Matador* represent?

   A. Argentina

   B. Ecuador

   C. Paraguay

   D. Uruguay

7. In Robin Van Persie's first season at Manchester United, he won the Premier League Golden Boot award. How many league goals did he score?

   A. 26

   B. 24

   C. 28

   D. 30

8. Which forward isn't a part of the 2020/2021 Manchester United squad?

   A. Federico Macheda

   B. Edinson Cavani

   C. Anthony Elanga

   D. Amad Diallo

9. Which national team does Manchester United forward, Anthony Martial, represent?

   A. Belgium

   B. France

   C. Portugal

   D. Sweden

10. Who was Manchester United's top goal scorer in the 2017/2018 season?

    A. Jesse Lingard

    B. Marcus Rashford

    C. Anthony Martial

    D. Romelu Lukaku

11. What nickname did Manchester United fans give to Eric Cantona?

    A. The Magician

    B. King Eric

    C. Flying Frenchman

    D. The Fox

12. Which Manchester United forward had the longest goalscoring streak in the Premier League?

    A. Cristiano Ronaldo

    B. Robin van Persie

    C. Wayne Rooney

    D. Ruud Van Nistelrooy

13. Who is the youngest ever Manchester United player to score a Premier League goal?

    A. Danny Welbeck

    B. Federico Macheda

    C. Marcus Rashford

    D. Mason Greenwood

14. Who was the first Manchester United player in Premier League history to score 5 goals in a Premier League match?

    A. Dimitar Berbatov

    B. Bobby Charlton

    C. Andrew Cole

    D. Cristiano Ronaldo

15. Who was Manchester United's top goal scorer in the 2011/2012 season?

    A. Dimitar Berbatov

    B. Wayne Rooney

    C. Javier Hernandez

    D. Michael Owen

16. Which club did Manchester United sign Ruud Van Nistelrooy from?

    A. PSV Eindhoven

    B. Herenveen

    C. Ajax Amsterdam

    D. Feyenoord

17. What was the nickname given to Mark Hughes by Manchester United fans?

    A. Marky

    B. Electric

    C. Main Mark

    D. Sparky

18. Which team did Andy Cole score his first league goal at Old Trafford against?

    A. Newcastle United

    B. Manchester United

    C. Manchester City

    D. Liverpool

19. Who is Manchester United's youngest forward to make a Premier League appearance?

    A. Danny Welbeck

    B. Federico Macheda

    C. Norman Whiteside

    D. Mason Greenwood

20. Which Manchester United player has the most Premier League goals in a single season?

    A. Cristiano Ronaldo

    B. Wayne Rooney

    C. Robin van Persie

    D. Ruud van Nistelrooy

20 Trivia Answers

1. C – Wayne Rooney
2. D – Ole Gunnar Solskjaer
3. B – Ole Gunnar Solskjaer
4. D – None
5. B – Javier Hernandez
6. D – Uruguay
7. A – 26
8. A – Federico Macheda
9. B – France
10. D – Romelu Lukaku
11. B – King Eric
12. D – Ruud Van Nistelrooy
13. B – Federico Macheda
14. C – Andrew Cole
15. B – Wayne Rooney
16. A – PSV Eindhoven
17. D – Sparky
18. B – Manchester United
19. D – Mason Greenwood
20. A – Cristiano Ronaldo

10 Fun Facts

1. Ruud Van Nistelrooy held the record for scoring in most consecutive games in the Premier League. He scored in 10 consecutive games between the 2002/03 and 2003/04 season. That was a Premier League record that stood until Jamie Vardy scored in 11 consecutive games in 2015. He also once scored 12 Champions League goals in 9 consecutive matches. In the 2002/03 season, Ruud Van Nistelrooy recorded his biggest goal tally for Manchester united – 44 goals in 52 games.
2. Ole Gunnar Solskjaer's nickname was the "babyface assassin" given his genial demeanor. He acquired a reputation for scoring after coming on as a substitute. On one occasion, he netted four times in 13 minutes after coming on against Nottingham Forest in the 1998/1999 season. Of course, he also scored the famous stoppage-time winner against Bayern Munich in the 1998/1999 UEFA Champions League final.
3. Cristiano Ronaldo holds the record for the highest number of Premier League goals scored in a season for Manchester United. He netted 31 goals in 38 matches in the 2007/2008 season.

4. Manchester United's most lethal trio in PL history was the Wayne Rooney (12), Carlos Tevez (14), and Cristiano Ronaldo (31) combo of 2007/08. They scored 57 goals within them.

5. Wayne Rooney is the club's highest goal scorer, with 253 goals in 559 games. His 208 PL goals make him the second-highest scorer in the competition history, second to only Alan Shearer. Wayne Rooney, with 53 goals in 120 appearances, is also England's record goal scorer. He is also the youngest ever scorer for the national team and was briefly the youngest ever goalscorer in the Euros

6. Dwight Yorke scored 123 PL goals in his career. That figure makes him the second most prolific PL goalscorer of non-European nationality, behind only Sergio Aguero.

7. Denis Law holds the record for most goals in a season for Manchester United. In the 1963/64 season, he scored 46 goals. He is also the only Scot to win the Ballon d'Or award.

8. With 32 league goals in the old Division 1 in 1959/60, Dennis Violet holds the club record for most league goals in a single league campaign.

9. In his first season at Manchester United, Robin Van Persie won the Premier League Golden Boot award with 26 goals. He formed a lethal partnership with Wayne Rooney that delivered Manchester United's last Premier League crown to date.

10. Apart from a highly successful time at Manchester United, striker, Andy Cole, also featured for seven other clubs in the top division – Arsenal, Blackburn Rovers, Manchester City, Portsmouth, Fulham, Newcastle United, and Sunderland. He is the third-highest ever PL goalscorer with 187 goals.

CAPTAINS

"Aggression is what I do. I go to war. You don't contest football matches with a reasonable state of mind."

-Roy Keane

20 Trivia Questions

1. Which of these Manchester United players was not a permanent club captain?
    A. Michael Carrick
    B. David Beckham
    C. Roy Keane
    D. Steve Bruce

2. Which player replaced Eric Cantona as captain?
    A. Ryan Giggs
    B. Michael Carrick
    C. Roy Keane
    D. Steve Bruce

3. Who captained Manchester United in the 2008 Champions League final?
    A. Edwin van der Sar
    B. Rio Ferdinand
    C. Michael Carrick
    D. Nemanja Vidic

4. Who is the current (2021/2022 season) captain of Manchester United?

    A. Paul Pogba

    B. Cristiano Ronaldo

    C. David de Gea

    D. Harry Maguire

5. Who wore the captain armband for Manchester United in the 2017 Europa League final win over Ajax Amsterdam?

    A. Chris Smalling

    B. Paul Pogba

    C. Ander Herrera

    D. Antonio Valencia

6. Who captained Manchester United alongside Steve Bruce between 1992 and 1994?

    A. Bryan Robson

    B. Bobby Charlton

    C. Eric Cantona

    D. Mark Hughes

7. Which Manchester United captain was nicknamed "Captain Fantastic" by fans?

    A. Roy Keane

    B. Bryan Robson

    C. Bobby Charlton

    D. Denis Law

8. Who was Manchester United's longest-ever serving captain?
    A. Nemanja Vidic
    B. Roy Keane
    C. Bryan Robson
    D. Gary Neville

9. What jersey number does the current captain of Manchester United hold?
    A. 23
    B. 6
    C. 5
    D. 15

10. How many Premier League titles did Manchester United win with Wayne Rooney as the club captain?
    A. 3
    B. 2
    C. 1
    D. None

11. Which player was Manchester United's captain from 2005-2011?
    A. Wayne Rooney
    B. Gary Neville
    C. Ryan Giggs
    D. Michael Carrick

12. Who was Manchester United's 8th captain in the Premier League era?
    A. Antonio Valencia
    B. Michael Carrick
    C. Gary Neville
    D. Harry Maguire

13. Who is the current (2021/2022 season) vice-captain of Manchester United?
    A. Bruno Fernandes
    B. Paul Pogba
    C. David de Gea
    D. Luke Shaw

14. In terms of major honours won, who is Manchester United's most successful captain?
    A. Bryan Robson
    B. Roy Keane
    C. Gary Neville
    D. Steve Bruce

15. Who was Manchester United's first captain of the premier league era?
    A. Bryan Robson
    B. Steve Bruce
    C. Denis Law
    D. Eric Cantona

16. Who captained Manchester United during the 1994 FA Cup final victory against Chelsea?

    A. Denis Law

    B. Steve Bruce

    C. Roy Keane

    D. Eric Cantona

17. How many seasons did Eric Cantona captain Manchester United for?

    A. 1

    B. 2

    C. 3

    D. 4

18. How many Premier League titles did Roy Keane win as a Manchester United captain?

    A. 6

    B. 5

    C. 4

    D. 3

19. What was Gary Neville's primary position on the field?

    A. Right Back

    B. Left Back

    C. Center Midfielder

    D. Forward

20. How many Premier League titles did Manchester United win with Nemanja Vidic as captain?

    A. 4

    B. 3

    C. 2

    D. 1

20 Trivia Answers

1. **B - David Beckham**
2. **C - Roy Keane**
3. **C - Rio Ferdinand**
4. **D - Harry Maguire**
5. **D - Antonio Valencia**
6. **B - Bryan Robson**
7. **A – Roy Keane**
8. **C – Bryan Robson**
9. **C – 5**
10. **D – None**
11. **B – Gary Neville**
12. **B – Michael Carrick**
13. **A – Bruno Fernandes**
14. **B – Roy Keane**
15. **A – Bryan Robson**
16. **B – Steve Bruce**
17. **A – 1**
18. **C – 4**
19. **A – Right Back**
20. **C – 2**

10 Fun Facts

1. Bryan Robson's 12 years of captaincy is the longest reign for any Manchester United captain. Fondly known as *Robbo, Captain Marvel, or Captain Courageous,* he played 466 times for United and scored 99 goals. He also captained England 65 times.
2. Manchester United has had 11 full-time captains in the Premier League era, starting from Bryan Robson in 1992, and the current captain is Harry Maguire.
3. Roy Keane is the most successful captain in the PL era, winning 4 Premier League titles, 2 FA Cups, and a Champions League trophy in 8 years. He was also the longest-serving captain under Sir Alex Ferguson.
4. Johnny Carey was appointed the captain by Sir Matt Busby in 1946 and was captain for seven years. He played in at least 9 different positions for the club, demonstrating great versatility. He was captain when the club won the league title for the first time in 41 seasons and also lifted the FA Cup and the Charity shield.
5. Roger Bryne, the Manchester United captain who died in the Munich disaster, almost singlehandedly reinvented the attacking fullback role. He led the club to two titles, won three tiles overall, and played 245 times. Who knows what else he might have achieved if his life was not cut short brutally?
6. Roy Keane is Manchester United's most contentious captain ever. He was a hard-tackling, hard-talking, and no-nonsense personality. His fondness for brutally honest takes landed him in trouble more than a few times. However, he also oversaw a great period for Manchester United and won 17 titles, including three Doubles.
7. Eric, "The King" Cantona, was the club's first non-British captain. He was only captain for the 1996/97 season, in which he led his team to the league title. He retired suddenly at the end of that season. He is fondly remembered for his larger-than-life image and goalscoring exploits that provided 82 goals in 5 years.

8. Wayne Rooney was the first appointed captain of the post-Ferguson era. He also won United's last major trophies – a league cup, FA Cup, and the Europa League title.
9. Gary Neville took over as club captain following Roy Keane's exit in 2005 and was the captain until 2011. A one-club man, he made 602 appearances for United over 20 years and scored 7 goals. He also made 117 appearances in the UCL for the club.
10. Harry Stafford was appointed captain in 1897, and his biggest act was saving the club from bankruptcy by convincing John Henry Davies to put cash into the struggling club.

TITLES

"I'm so proud the fans still sing my name, but I fear tomorrow they will stop. I fear it because I love it. And everything you love; you fear you will lose."

-Eric Cantona

20 Trivia Questions

1. How many Premier League titles did Sir Alex win at Manchester United?

    A. 15

    B. 11

    C. 17

    D. 13

2. How many UEFA Champions League titles has Manchester United won?

    A. 4

    B. 2

    C. 3

    D. 1

3. In which year did Manchester United win their first-ever European cup?

    A. 1968

    B. 1982

    C. 1972

    D. 1978

4. Which team did Manchester United defeat in the final to win their first European Cup?

    A. Benfica

    B. AC Milan

    C. Ajax Amsterdam

    D. Real Madrid

5. Which club did Manchester United defeat in the 2008 UEFA Champions League final?

    A. Liverpool

    B. Barcelona

    C. Chelsea

    D. AC Milan

6. How many times has Manchester United won the English FA Cup?

    A. 13

    B. 12

    C. 11

    D. 10

7. As of 2021, how many times has Manchester United won the English league title?

    A. 22

    B. 21

    C. 20

    D. 19

8. When last did Manchester United win the Premier League title?

   A. 2012

   B. 2013

   C. 2011

   D. 2010

9. In what year did Manchester United win their first-ever FIFA Club World Cup?

   A. 2012

   B. 2010

   C. 2008

   D. 2006

10. What was the score line (a.e.t) when Manchester United won their first-ever European Cup final against Benfica?

    A. 4 – 1

    B. 2 – 1

    C. 2 – 0

    D. 3 – 1

11. How many times has Manchester United won the UEFA Europa League?

    A. 4

    B. 3

    C. 2

    D. 1

12. Which of these trophies did Manchester United fail to win in her treble-winning season?

    A. Premier League

    B. English FA Cup

    C. League Cup

    D. UEFA Champions League

13. In which season did Manchester United win the treble?

    A. 2008-2009

    B. 1998-1999

    C. 2002-2003

    D. 1992-1993

14. In which of these years did Manchester United fail to win the Premier League title twice in a row?

    A. 1995/1996 & 1996/1997

    B. 1999/2000 & 2000/2001

    C. 2000/2001 & 2001/2002

    D. 2006/2007 & 2007/2008

15. How many times has Man Utd won the Premier League title thrice in a row?

    A. Once

    B. Twice

    C. Thrice

    D. None

16. What is the highest point Manchester United has won a Premier League title with?

    A. 94

    B. 92

    C. 90

    D. 88

17. In what year did Manchester United win her first League Cup?

    A. 1990

    B. 1991

    C. 1992

    D. 1993

18. In which season did Manchester United win the Premier League and League Cup?

    A. 1993/1994

    B. 2007/2008

    C. 1998/1999

    D. 2008/2009

19. As of 2021, what was the last trophy Manchester United won?

    A. UEFA Europa League

    B. English Premier League

    C. FA Cup

    D. League Cup

20. How many times have Manchester United won the FIFA Club World Cup?

    A. 4

    B. 3

    C. 2

    D. 1

20 Trivia Answers

1. **D - 13**
2. **B - 2**
3. **A - 1968**
4. **A - Benfica**
5. **C - Chelsea**
6. **B - 12**
7. **C - 20**
8. **B - 2013**
9. **C - 2008**
10. **A - 4 – 1**
11. **D - 1**
12. **C - League Cup**
13. **B - 1998-1999**
14. **C - 2000/2001 & 2001/2002**
15. **B - twice**
16. **B - 92** (42 premier league matches were played instead of 38 in their 1993/1994 premier league winning campaign)
17. C - **1992**
18. **D - 2008/2009**
19. **A - UEFA Europa League**
20. **D - 1**

10 Fun Facts

1. Sir Alex Ferguson's Manchester United won 13 premier league titles in 28 seasons – the most of any manager.
2. Manchester United is the only English club to win the treble of UCL, PL, and FA cup titles in a single season. This feat was achieved in the 1998/99 season.
3. Manchester United also won the Premier League three times in a row between the 1998/99 and 2000/01 seasons. This also marked only the fourth time an English club had won the league title for three consecutive seasons. The club repeated the feat between the 2006/07 and 2008/09 seasons with three consecutive league titles.
4. Manchester United has won 20 first division titles (13 EPL), 12 FA Cups, 5 League cups, 3 European Cup/UEFA Champions League, 1 UEFA winners' cup, and 1 UEFA Europa League titles
5. In the 1993/94 season, Manchester United won its first Double (The FA cup and league titles in the same season). The feat was repeated in the 1995/96 season, and United became the first club to win the Double twice.
6. The club won its first league title in 1908, two seasons after promotion to the First Division.
7. Manchester United is one of only 5 sides to have won all three UEFA titles – the Champions League, the Super Cup, and Europa League.
8. Manchester United's highest accrued points to win the Premier League was 92 points in 1993/94.
9. The club's highest league winning margin was 18 points in the 1999/2000 season.
10. In December 2008, Manchester United became the first Premier League side to win the FIFA Club World Cup after defeating LDU Quito 2-1 in the final in Yokohama, Japan.

MEMORABLE GAMES

"When the seagulls follow the trawler, it is because they think sardines will be thrown into the sea."

-Eric Cantona

20 Trivia Questions

1. Against which club did Manchester United record their biggest win (7:1) in the Champions League?

    A. Benfica

    B. Monaco

    C. AS Roma

    D. PSV Eindhoven

2. Manchester United achieved her biggest Premier League win against Ipswich Town. What was the scoreline?

    A. 8 -1

    B. 9 – 1

    C. 8 – 0

    D. 9 – 0

3. Manchester United's first-ever league cup match was against which club?

    A. Blackburn Rovers

    B. Sunderland

    C. Exeter

    D. Hull City

4. How many goals did Wayne Rooney score on his Manchester United debut?

   A. 4

   B. 3

   C. 2

   D. 1

5. Which Manchester United player scored during extra time to win the 2016 FA Cup Final?

   A. Marcus Rashford

   B. Anthony Martial

   C. Memphis Depay

   D. Jesse Lingard

6. Which team did Manchester United first face at Old Trafford?

   A. Liverpool

   B. Blackburn Rovers

   C. Arsenal

   D. Nottingham Forest

7. What was the scoreline of Manchester United's record FA Cup win?

   A. 6 – 0

   B. 7 – 0

   C. 8 – 0

   D. 9 – 0

8. Who scored the winner for Manchester United against Bayern Munich in the 1999 European Cup final?

   A. Teddy Sheringham

   B. Ole Gunnar Solskjaer

   C. David Beckham

   D. Ruud van Nistelrooy

9. In the Manchester Derby match on the 7th of April 2018, who scored an unlikely winner for Manchester United?

   A. Paul Pogba

   B. Marcus Rashford

   C. Mason Greenwood

   D. Chris Smalling

10. Which club did Manchester United play against immediately after the death of Sir Matt Busby?

   A. Everton

   B. Newcastle United

   C. Blackburn Rovers

   D. Wigan Athletic

11. Who scored the winner for Manchester United against Juventus in the 1999 Champions League semi-final second leg?

   A. Ole Gunnar Solskjaer

   B. Ryan Giggs

   C. Andrew Cole

   D. Paul Scholes

12. With just two minutes left on the clock, who scored the equalizing goal for Manchester United against Liverpool in the 1994 FA Cup 4th Round?

    A. Dwight Yorke

    B. Paul Scholes

    C. Andrew Cole

    D. Mark Hughes

13. Who scored Manchester United's last goal in the 5:3 comeback win against Tottenham Hotspur in the 2001/2002 premier league season?

    A. Juan Sebastian Veron

    B. Andrew Cole

    C. David Beckham

    D. Ruud van Nistelrooy

14. In the 2010/11 Premier League season, which team did Wayne Rooney score a hattrick against within 14 minutes?

    A. Derby County

    B. Norwich

    C. Burnley

    D. West Ham

15. After just 11 minutes, Manchester United trailed Juventus by two goals in the second leg of the 1999 Champions League semi-final. What was the final score line?

    A. 4:3

    B. 3:2

    C. 3:3

    D. 5:3

16. What was the aggregate score when Manchester United defeated Barcelona in the 1984 European Cup Winners quarter-final match?

    A. 2:0

    B. 3:1

    C. 3:2

    D. 4:1

17. In the 2011/2012 Premier League season, Manchester United staged a late comeback against Chelsea by scoring how many goals in 20 minutes?

    A. 5

    B. 4

    C. 3

    D. 2

18. In the 1999 Champions League Final match against Bayern Munich, Manchester United staged a comeback. What was the final score line?

    A. 2:1

    B. 3:2

    C. 4:3

    D. 4:2

19. On the 12th of February 2011, which player scored an iconic goal to give Manchester United a Manchester Derby win?

    A. Nani

    B. Wayne Rooney

    C. Dimitar Berbatov

    D. Antonio Valencia

20. In August 2011, Manchester United inflicted Arsenal's heaviest defeat since 1896. What was the scoreline?

    A. 6:0

    B. 7:1

    C. 8:2

    D. 8:1

20 Trivia Answers

1. C - AS Roma
2. D - 9 – 0
3. C - Exeter
4. B - 3
5. D - Jesse Lingard
6. A - Liverpool
7. C - 8 – 0
8. B - Ole Gunnar Solskjaer
9. D - Chris Smalling
10. A - Everton
11. C - Andrew Cole
12. A - Dwight Yorke
13. C - David Beckham
14. D - West Ham
15. B - 3:2
16. C - 3:2
17. C - 3
18. A - 2:1
19. B - Rooney
20. C - 8:2

10 Fun Facts

1. Manchester United defeated Bayern Munich 2-1 in the 1998/99 UCL final to win their first-ever UCL. Going into stoppage time, the game was locked at 1-0 in favour of Bayern Munich, but the game ended dramatically after the pair of Teddy Sheringham and Ole Gunnar Solskjaer scored in stoppage time to turn the game around.
2. The 2008 UEFA Champions League final win against Chelsea was the first all-English final, and what a match it was. Cristiano Ronaldo gave United the lead with a first-half header, but Frank Lampard stole in, to equalize shortly before half-time. Despite big chances, neither team could score, and the game went to a penalty shootout after 120 minutes. Ronaldo missed his penalty, but John Terry could not capitalize as he slipped to miss his penalty too. In sudden death, Ryan Giggs gave the Red Devils the advantage, and Edwin Van der Sar then saved dramatically from Nicolas Anelka to secure United's second UCL trophy on a cold night in Moscow.
3. In a 2001 Premier League game, Manchester United was down to Tottenham Spurs by 3-0 at half-time. In the second half, the game changed. Andy Cole scored immediately after half-time, and Laurent Blanc gave United further hope. Nistelrooy equalized, and Juan Sebastian Veron finished on his weaker foot to give United the lead. David Beckham then struck a perfect finish into the far corner to give Manchester United a 5-3 win.
4. After losing 2-1 to AS Roma in the first leg of the 2006/07 UCL quarter-finals, Manchester United had it all to do at Old Trafford. And how they did it. Needing only a 1-0 win to proceed on away goal rules, the Red Devils ran riot. Michael Carrick opened the scoring; Alan Smith doubled the lead, and Wayne Rooney and Cristiano Ronaldo weighed in with goals in the first half. A second-half worldie from Michael Carrick, another Ronaldo finish, and a

smart Evra finish meant that De Rossi's goal for AS Roma was no more than a consolation. 7-1 it finished!

5. In the 2010/2011 season, West Ham needed three points in their fight against relegation, and United needed a win to avoid losing more ground to an Arsenal team that had a game in hand. United went down 2-0 until the 64th minute, but a barnstorming finish saw them win 4-2.

6. On the 25th of January, 1995, a scene that had never been seen erupted in the Manchester United vs. Crystal Palace match at Selhurst Park. Eric Cantona was sent off for the Reds for kicking Richard Shaw out of frustration. As he trudged off the pitch, he suddenly launched a Kung Fu kick at Palace supporter, Matthew Simmons, who had run down the stairs to confront and abuse *King Eric.* The event's aftermath shook Manchester United and English football to its core. Cantona was banned for 8 months worldwide, dismissed from the French National team, fined, and prosecuted for assault. He was sentenced to 120 hours of community service after an appeal.

7. In the 1998/99 season, Arsenal and Manchester United had another go at the hot rivalry. In the FA cup semi-final replay, Dennis Bergkamp and David Beckham scored to leave the match tied at 1-1. Roy Keane was then dismissed; Dennis Bergkamp took a late penalty, but Edwin Van der Sar saved his effort, and the game went into extra time. Deep into extra time, Ryan Giggs took possession of the ball and went on a mesmeric run that ended with him beating the entire Arsenal backline and shooting past David Seaman to win the game. He took off his shirt to celebrate, and the world was introduced to his copious chest hair in one of the most iconic FA cup images.

8. The league match between Arsenal and Manchester United in September 2003 ended in uproar. Firstly, Arsenal captain Patrick Viera, was sent off for a tangle with Ruud Van Nistelrooy. Then, defender, Martin Keown, was adjudged to have brought down Diego Forlan. Arsenal protested what they felt was a blatant dive. Van Nistelrooy stepped up to take the penalty and sent the ball cannoning off the crossbar. Jubilant Arsenal fans surrounded and goaded the United forward, and chaos ensued. The FA responded by charging six Arsenal fans with improper conduct.

9. In October 2004, Arsenal visited Old Trafford on a record 49 matches unbeaten

run, which their eternal rivals were pumped up to end. In a game fraught with hard tackles and bad blood, Arsenal had the slight upper hand. But then, Wayne Rooney was adjudged to have been fouled by Sol Campbell, and Nistelrooy had the chance to make amends for his miss the previous season. He didn't make a mistake this time. Shortly before the end of the game, Wayne Rooney doubled United's advantage for a comprehensive win. At the end of the game, emotions took over in the tunnel. Wenger took exception to a hard tackle Van Nistelrooy had made on Ashley Cole, and Sir Alex Ferguson intervened to defend his star forward. An unidentified Arsenal player then threw Pizza at Sir Alex. The event is dubbed *Pizzagate,* but no real investigations took place. Cesc Fabregas has since owned up to throwing the Pizza.

10. Yet another heated match with Arsenal took place in the return leg of the 2004/05 season. Viera was alleged to have confronted and pushed Gary Neville during the pregame warmup in retaliation over challenges Pires had suffered in the first game. When Roy Keane learned of this confrontation, he took on Viera in the tunnel before the game, and both men had to be physically restrained. The game that followed was another ill-tempered affair with numerous flying tackles, and Manchester United had Mikael Silvestre sent off for a clash with Freddie Ljungberg. However, United came from behind twice to win the game.

11. The 1968 European Cup final saw Benfica square up to the Red Devils at the Wembley Stadium in front of 92, 225 supporters. Sir Bobby Charlton gave United the lead in the 53rd minute, but Jaime Graca equalized for Benfica 26 minutes later. The game then went into extra time, and Manchester United scored three times in 7 minutes through George Best, Brian Kidd, and Charlton to claim their first European Cup, the first for any English club.

BIGGEST TRANSFERS

"Manchester United breathes football. When I have to make hard decisions, I always listen to the little boy inside me and what he wants. That little boy was screaming for United."

-Robin Van Persie

20 Trivia Questions

1. Which player holds the current record of the most expensive sale in the history of Manchester United?

    A. Romelu Lukaku

    B. Paul Pogba

    C. Cristiano Ronaldo

    D. Wayne Rooney

2. Who is the most expensive player in the history of Manchester United?

    A. Harry Maguire

    B. Paul Pogba

    C. Cristiano Ronaldo

    D. Bruno Fernandez

3. How many times has Manchester United broken the British transfer record?

    A. 9 times

    B. 10 times

    C. 3 times

    D. Once

4. What year did Manchester United sign Cristiano Ronaldo from Sporting Lisbon?

   A. 2002

   B. 2001

   C. 2004

   D. 2003

5. Which Manchester United player is the most expensive defender in the world?

   A. Aaron Wan Bissaka

   B. Luke Shaw

   C. Harry Maguire

   D. Eric Bailly

6. In 2020, Manchester United signed Bruno Fernandes from which club?

   A. FC Porto

   B. SC Braga

   C. Benfica

   D. Sporting CP

7. Which player is the third most expensive sale in the history of Manchester United?

   A. Romelu Lukaku

   B. Angel Di Maria

   C. Memphis Depay

   D. David Beckham

8. Which player is the third most expensive signing in the history of Manchester United?

    A. Romelu Lukaku

    B. Bruno Fernandes

    C. Jadon Sancho

    D. Aaron Wan Bissaka

9. Which club did Manchester United sign Donny van de Beek from?

    A. Barcelona

    B. Ajax Amsterdam

    C. Real Betis

    D. Leipzig

10. As of 2021, who is the highest-paid Manchester United player?

    A. David de Gea

    B. Paul Pogba

    C. Cristiano Ronaldo

    D. Jadon Sancho

11. Who was Manchester United's most expensive signing in 2018?

    A. Bruno Fernandes

    B. Anthony Martial

    C. Romelu Lukaku

    D. Fred

12. Which of these players is not among Manchester United's top 10 most expensive signing?

    A. Fred

    B. Juan Mata

    C. Rio Ferdinand

    D. Anthony Martial

13. Who was Manchester United's least expensive signing of the 2021/2022 summer transfer window?

    A. Raphael Varane

    B. Cristiano Ronaldo

    C. Tom Heaton

    D. Jadon Sancho

14. As of 2021, who is Manchester United's most expensive forward signing?

    A. Romelu Lukaku

    B. Jadon Sancho

    C. Angel di Maria

    D. Bruno Fernandes

15. Who was Manchester United's most expensive sale of the 2021/2022 summer transfer window?

    A. Andreas Pereira

    B. Joel Pereira

    C. Brandon Williams

    D. Daniel James

16. Aaron Wan Bissaka arrived at Manchester United for a transfer fee of €50m. Which club was he signed from?

    A. Crystal Palace

    B. West Bromwich Albion

    C. Brighton and Hove Albion

    D. West Ham

17. Who was Manchester United's most expensive signing of the 2020/21 season?

    A. Alex Telles

    B. Edinson Cavani

    C. Donny van de Beek

    D. Amad Diallo

18. Which of these players joined Manchester United as a free agent?

    A. Edinson Cavani

    B. Amad Diallo

    C. Diogo Dalot

    D. Alan Smith

19. Who is the second most expensive Manchester United's defender?

    A. Raphael Varane

    B. Aaron Wan-Bissaka

    C. Eric Baily

    D. Rio Ferdinand

20. Who was Manchester United's most expensive signing in 2015?

    A. Anthony Martial

    B. Juan Sebastian Veron

    C. Dimitar Berbatov

    D. Rio Ferdinand

20 Trivia Answers

1. C – Cristiano Ronaldo
2. B – Paul Pogba
3. B – 10 times
4. D – 2003
5. C – Harry Maguire
6. D – Sporting CP
7. B – Angel Di Maria
8. A – Romelu Lukaku
9. B – Ajax Amsterdam
10. C – Cristiano Ronaldo
11. D – Fred
12. B – Juan Mata
13. C – Tom Heaton
14. A – Romelu Lukaku
15. D – Daniel James
16. A – Crystal Palace
17. C – Donny van de Beek
18. A – Edinson Cavani
19. B – Aaron Wan-Bissaka
20. A – Anthony Martial

10 Fun Facts

1. Leeds Chairman, Bill Fotherby, had called his Manchester United counterpart, Martin Edwards, to see if Dennis Irwin might be sold to him. The Manchester United chief and Sir Alex were in a meeting when the call came in, and Sir Alex jokingly inquired if Leeds might be willing to sell Cantona to United. Fotherby paused, consulted with his manager, and sanctioned Cantona's sale to Manchester United. The rest is history.

2. Harry Maguire's £80 million transfer is not the first time Manchester United has broken the British transfer record for a defender. Rio Ferdinand's £29.1 million fee to Leeds City was a record in 2003.

3. After Nottingham Forest was relegated in the 1992/1993 season, Blackburn Manager, Kenny Dalglish, encouraged Roy Keane to make a move to his club. A £4m fee was agreed on a Friday, and all parties were eager to complete the move. However, a mistake was discovered in the contract that prevented it from being signed that day. All parties agreed to meet on the next Monday to fix this, but Sir Alex Ferguson heard of the impending transfer and reached out to Roy Keane to convince him to join United instead. A £3.75m deal was concluded on Saturday and Roy Keane joined the Red Devils instead. The rest is history, as they say.

4. Paul Pogba's £89.3 million transfer fee is still the highest that Manchester United has ever paid for a player. The fee allowed the talented Frenchman to rejoin the club he had left as a teenager.

5. Ronaldo's £80 million sale to Madrid is still the highest transfer fee that United has ever pocketed. The closest fee is the £73 million Inter Milan paid to take Romelu Lukaku to the Serie A.

6. Manchester United has signed seven Brazilian players in the past but also had near misses with several *Samba* stars. The Red Devils attempted to sign Ronaldo

and Ronaldinho but lost out to Barcelona on both occasions. Manchester United also failed with a more recent attempt to sign Lucas Moura.

7. Javier Hernandez Chicharito cost a mere £6 million when he joined Manchester United in 2010. His goalscoring exploits for the Red Devils made the fee seem paltry and inconsequential.

8. On his return to Manchester United in 2021, Ronaldo's number 7 jerseys sold $60 million in the first 24 hours. That was a club and brand record that is likely to stand for some time.

9. In January 1995, Newcastle United manager Kevin Keegan, suddenly sanctioned the sale of young star, Andy Cole, to fierce rivals, Manchester United, in a £7m deal that valued Cole at £6m and involved Keith Gillespie moving to Newcastle. Cole had scored 68 goals in 84 matches for Newcastle United at this point and went on to play a huge part in transforming Manchester United into the dominant PL force for the next decade and beyond.

10. In 2002, Arsenal manager, Arsene Wenger met with Cristiano Ronaldo at the Highbury stadium to convince him to move to Arsenal. The player had also been offered to Barcelona's President, Joan Laporta, and Liverpool's manager, Gerard Houllier. However, after a friendly match in August 2003 between Sporting CP and Manchester United, Sir Alex Ferguson was so impressed by the young star that he immediately signed him for £12.27m. The aftermath of the story is well-known.

RECORD BREAKERS

"Manchester United might not win the Premier League every year, but we'd always be up there competing for it every year."

-Sir Alex Ferguson

SHARP

20 Trivia Questions

1. Who was the first-ever Manchester United player to win the PFA young player of the year award?

    A. Nicky Butt

    B. David Beckham

    C. Ryan Giggs

    D. Lee Sharpe

2. Who scored the fastest four goals for Manchester United in a single Premier League match?

    A. Ruud van Nistelrooy

    B. Ole Gunnar Solksjaer

    C. Bobby Charlton

    D. Ryan Giggs

3. Who is the oldest player to ever play for Manchester United in the Premier League era?

    A. Edwin van der Sar

    B. Ryan Giggs

    C. Paul Scholes

    D. Raymond van der Gouw

4. How many matches was Manchester United's longest unbeaten run?

   A. 28

   B. 29

   C. 30

   D. 27

5. Which of these Manchester United players has won the European Golden boot?

   A. Robin van Persie

   B. Cristiano Ronaldo

   C. Wayne Rooney

   D. Ruud van Nistelrooy

6. Which of these Manchester United players has the most appearances for the club?

   A. Ryan Giggs

   B. Bobby Charlton

   C. Paul Scholes

   D. Wayne Rooney

7. Who is Manchester United's most red-carded player of all time?

   A. Nemanja Vidic

   B. Roy Keane

   C. Eric Baily

   D. Paul Scholes

8. Which Manchester United goalkeeper has kept the most consecutive clean sheets?

   A. Harry Gregg

   B. Jimmy Rimmer

   C. Peter Schmeichel

   D. Edwin Van Der Sar

9. Which Manchester United player holds the record of FA cup appearances for the club?

   A. Ryan Giggs

   B. Bobby Charlton

   C. Paul Scholes

   D. Wayne Rooney

10. Who scored Manchester United's fastest goal in the premier league?

    A. Ruud van Nistelrooy

    B. Ole Gunnar Solksjaer

    C. Bobby Charlton

    D. Ryan Giggs

11. Which Manchester United player is the all-time top scorer in Europe?

    A. Eric Cantona

    B. Wayne Rooney

    C. Ruud van Nistelrooy

    D. Ryan Giggs

12. As of 2021, who is the non-British Manchester United player with the most appearances?

    A. Patrice Evra

    B. Peter Schmeichel

    C. David de Gea

    D. Antonio Valencia

13. Which of these players won the Ballon d'Or at Manchester United?

    A. George Best

    B. Ruud Van Nistelrooy

    C. David Beckham

    D. Wayne Rooney

14. Which Manchester United player won the PFA Player's Player of the year in 2000?

    A. Roy Keane

    B. Teddy Sheringham

    C. Ruud van Nistelrooy

    D. Mark Hughes

15. How many Manchester United players have won the Ballon d'Or

    A. 6

    B. 4

    C. 2

    D. 1

16. Who was the first-ever Manchester United player to be sent off in an FA Cup Final?

    A. Kevin Moran

    B. Nicky Butt

    C. Mark Hughes

    D. Eric Bailly

17. How long was Manchester United's longest clean sheet streak?

    A. 11 games

    B. 13 games

    C. 12 games

    D. 14 games

18. Which Manchester United player made the shortest Premier League appearance?

    A. Sammy Mcllroy

    B. Chris Smalling

    C. Luke Shaw

    D. David Gaskell

19. Which of these Manchester United players has the most consecutive league appearances?

    A. Ryan Giggs

    B. Wayne Rooney

    C. Steve Coppell

    D. Ruud van Nistelrooy

20. Which of these Manchester United players has won the FIFA Puskas Award?

    A. David Beckham

    B. Cristiano Ronaldo

    C. Henrikh Mkhitaryan

    D. Ruud van Nistelrooy

20 Trivia Answers

1. C – Ryan Giggs
2. B – Ole Gunnar Solksjaer
3. A – Edwin van der Sar
4. B – 29
5. B – Cristiano Ronaldo
6. A – Ryan Giggs
7. B – Roy Keane
8. D – Edwin van der Sar
9. B – Bobby Charlton
10. D – Ryan Giggs
11. B – Wayne Rooney
12. C – David de Gea
13. A – George Best
14. A – Roy Keane
15. B – 4
16. A – Kevin Moran
17. D – 11 games
18. B – Chris Smalling
19. C – Steve Coppell
20. B – Cristiano Ronaldo

10 Fun Facts

1. Despite only playing half the season in 2019/20, Bruno Fernandes' 12 goals and 8 assists were the 4th highest goal contributions in the squad. He also won the Premier League's Goal of the Month and Player of the Month awards concurrently, becoming the first-ever player to achieve the feat. He also became the first Manchester United player to win consecutive Player of the Month awards and ended the season as the Europa League top scorer.
2. Ryan Giggs is Manchester United's most capped player with 963 total appearances, including 672 league appearances, 74 FA cup appearances, 157 European appearances, 41 League Cup appearances, and 19 appearances in other competitions. He also has the most Premier League winners medal (13) and the highest number of seasons played (22).
3. Edwin Van der Sar is Manchester United's oldest ever post-Second World War player. He was 40 years, 211 days old when he lined up against Barcelona in the 2011 Champions League. He also holds the record for the longest consecutive clean sheets in the Premier League (14).
4. Two different players have scored 5 goals in one match while playing for Manchester United. They are Dimitar Berbatov vs. Blackburn Rovers (2010) and Andrew Cole vs. Ipswich (1995).
5. Ronaldo is the only Manchester United player to win a Ballon d'Or (2008) in the Premier League era. Other winners at United include Denis Law (1964), Bobby Charlton (1966), and George Best (1968). Aside from the Ballon d'Or, Ronaldo has also won the Puskas (2009) and FIFA player of the year (2008) awards as a Manchester United player.
6. David Beckham was the Ballon d'Or runner-up in 1999 when he won the UEFA Club Footballer player of the year as a Manchester United player. He also came second in voting for the FIFA World Player of the Year in 1999 and

2001. He was voted into the PFA Team of the Year for four consecutive seasons from the 1996/97 season to the 1999/00 season. David Beckham was also the first British player to record 100 appearances in the UEFA Champions League.

7. Wayne Rooney remains the club's highest goal scorer, with 253 goals from 559 appearances. The breakdown is 183 (league), 22 (FA), 5(league cup), 39 (Europe) and 4 goals in other competitions. He surpassed Sir Bobby Charlton's longstanding record of 249 goals on the 21st of January, 2017, with a free-kick equalizer against Stoke City.

8. Manchester United's biggest win of the Premier League era is a 9-0 win against Ipswich town in 1995. They repeated this feat in a February 2021 win over Southampton. Manchester United's record league win, though, is a 10-1 defeat of Wolverhampton Wanderers in the old First Division in October 1892. The record European win and overall club record is a 10-0 win over Anderlecht in the European Cup Preliminary round in 1956. The record Champions league win is the 7-1 defeat of Roma in April 2007.

9. Manchester United's biggest loss of the Premier League era is a pair of 6-1 defeats to Manchester City in 2011 and Tottenham Hotspurs in 2020. However, United has also been on the wrong end of three 7-0 losses to Wolverhampton Wanderers, Aston Villa, and Blackburn Rovers.

10. Manchester United's longest unbeaten run in major competitions stands at 45 matches across December 1998 to October 1999. The longest unbeaten run in the league is 29 matches set between December 1998 to September 1999 and matched between April 2010 and February 2011.

A Short Message from The House of Ballers team

Hello fellow sports fanatic, we hope you enjoyed *The Best Manchester United Trivia Book Ever.*

We'd like to thank you for purchasing and reading it to the end.

We create these books to allow people to, not just expand their knowledge around their favorite clubs and players, but also to keep the passion we all have for the game lit and alive.

Life can come with many challenges and setbacks. But something that never leaves our side is our love for the game. If you enjoyed reading this book, we'd like to kindly ask for your feedback and thoughts in the review section on Amazon.com.

This will help us continue to make the highest quality books and content for fans all across the world.

>> Scan the QR Code below with your smartphone to leave a short review <<

Ball out,

The House of Ballers Team